WISHBONE™

Activity Book

EmBARK on Adventure!

Modern Publishing
A Division of Unisystems, Inc.
New York, New York 10022
Printed in the U.S.A.
2 4 6 8 10 9 7 5 3
UPC Number: 10770
ISBN Number: 1-56144-999-7

The Adventures of Tom Sawyer

Tom Sawyer and Huckleberry Finn sneak into the graveyard late one night and witness a crime. Unscramble the words below, and read down to see who wrote this American classic!

IDMIGHNT

midnight

(The spookiest hour)

TARWS warts

(Huck wants to cure these bumps)

SDARSKEN

Darkness

(What you find when there is no light)

HIIDGN Hiding

(What Tom and Huck are doing here)

MBTOTOSNE

Tombstone

(A grave marker)

MARK Twain

See answer #1

Aunt Polly wonders what Tom Sawyer will explore today. Follow the path to help him get to school where he belongs!

See answer #2

Tom is on the witness stand because he knows who the real criminal is! Cross out the word TOM every time you see it to learn the culprit's name.

Tom Sawyer and Becky Thatcher get lost in a cave! Can you help them find their way out?

See answer #4

The Thousand and One Arabian Nights

The King of Persia orders beautiful Shahrazad to her doom! Wishbone wags his tail because he knows how she will cleverly save her own life. Fill in all the squares with a W, A, or G to discover what it is.

G	W	S	H	E	W	G	A	W	M	U	S	T	W	A
W	T	E	L	L	A	H	I	M	G	W	A	G	W	G
A	S	G	T	W	O	A	R	W	I	G	E	A	S	W

See answer #5

Ali Baba wants to learn the magic words that will open the secret cave of the Forty Thieves! Read up, down, backwards, forwards, and diagonally to find and circle the words on the list. The letters you *don't circle* will give Ali Baba his answer!

```
B A B A L I
C O P E N A
A F E I H T
V L T A L E
E Y T R O F
S E S A M E
```

ALI
BABA
CAVE
FORTY
THIEF
FLY
TALE
ATE

See answer #6

Ali Baba's greedy brother Kasim forgot the secret words that will allow him to escape the cave! Follow the dots to see what Kasim had hoped to take with him.

See answer #7

You'll find magic carpets in other stories from *The Thousand and One Arabian Nights*. Imagine Wishbone taking a ride on a flying carpet and then find the matching one.

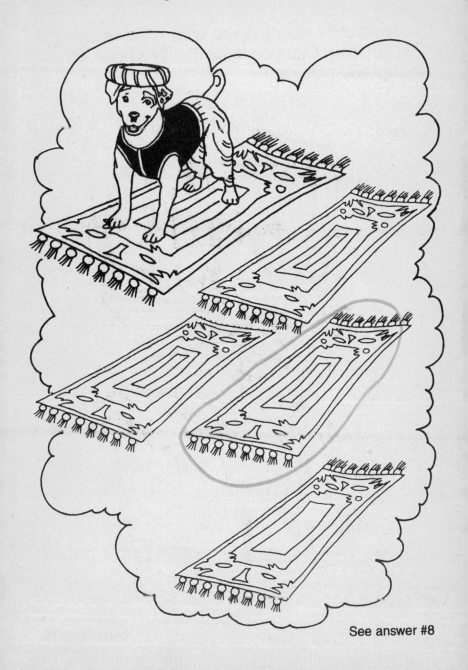

See answer #8

The Odyssey

Odysseus is sailing home after his victory in the Trojan War. Can you circle 5 differences between these two pictures?

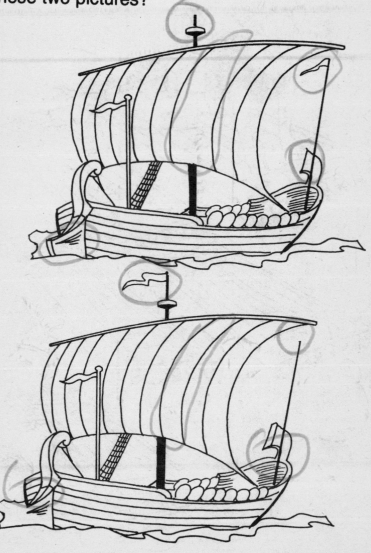

See answer #9

To keep Odysseus from leaving, the enchantress Circe has turned his men into pigs! Can you number the pictures in the right order to change them back?

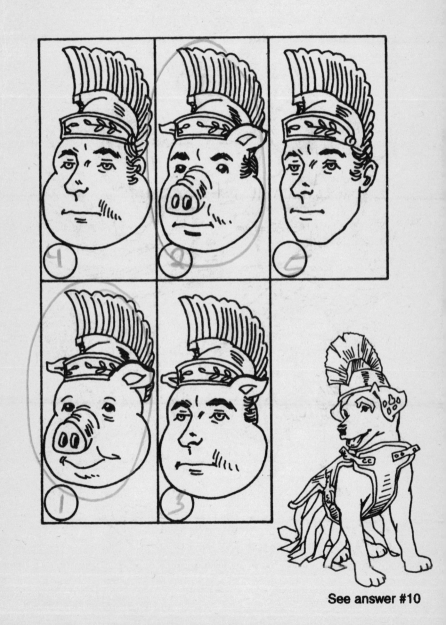

See answer #10

Odysseus needs to hide his men from the Cyclops.
Can you guess where they are hiding?
Circle them.

See answer #11

The Sirens sing to lure sailors onto the rocks. Odysseus has his men tie him to the mast so he can't answer their call. Can you count the number of singing Sirens?

See answer #12

The Three Musketeers

D'Artagnan loves to practice fencing. Can you find all 6 swords in this picture? Circle them!

See answer #13

The Three Musketeers help D'Artagnan battle the Cardinal's evil henchmen. Can you solve this crossword puzzle about the fine art of fencing?

DOWN
1. The Musketeers' home and capital of France
2. The sharp tip of a sword
3. Another name for sword

ACROSS
4. A Musketeer's weapon
5. The art of sword fighting

See answer #14

The beautiful but evil Milady tries to win D'Artagnan over to the Cardinal's side, but he won't betray his friends! Fill in all the squares that have the letters F, I, N, or D to see what D'Artagnan wants to be.

F	I	D	N	I	D	F	A	D	F	I	D	N	F
I	D	N	L	F	O	D	Y	I	A	N	L	F	D
F	M	U	N	S	K	I	E	T	E	D	E	N	R

See answer #15

D'Artagnan has been accused of treason! The Cardinal will release him if he has a special document called a carte blanche. Can you help D'Artagnan find it?

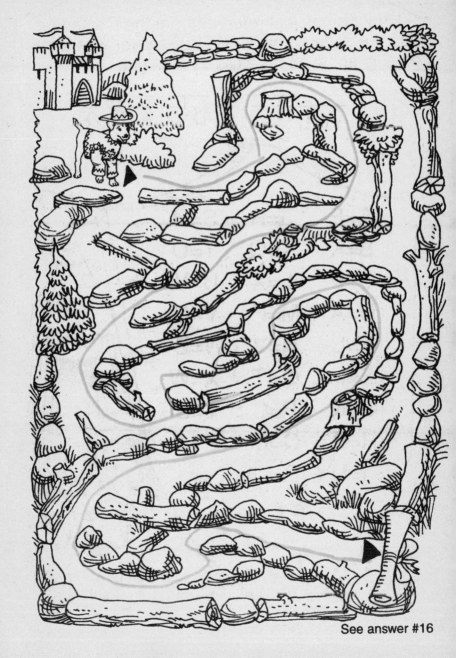

See answer #16

Ivanhoe

Ivanhoe has just returned from the Crusades. Use the code on his shield to discover where he goes to show off his skills as a knight.

Tournament

O T I J G D Q A G O

A=E J=R S=H
B=K K=Q T=O
C=P L=X U=Y
D=A M=F V=G
E=L N=V W=Z
F=I O=T X=W
G=N P=C Y=S
H=B Q=M Z=J
I=U R=D

See answer #17

Ivanhoe is a brave Saxon knight in medieval England. He has just beaten the Norman knight, Sir Brian, in archery and swordsmanship. Draw lines to match the weapons below to each other.

See answer #18

Rebecca rescues Ivanhoe and takes him home in her caravan after he is wounded in the tournament. But he's not safe yet. Unscramble the words below, and then read the boxed letters to discover who is going to attack!

THE ATTACKER: Sir Brian

Scramble	Answer	Clue
WOSRD	Sword	A knight's weapon
DERI	Ride	What knights do on horses
SEHOR	Horse	A knight's mount
AVERB	Brave	Not cowardly
ACCEBRE	Rebecca	Ivanhoe's new friend
HOEVNAI	Ivanhoe	The title of this novel
VESA	Save	To rescue
SNOXSA	Saxose	Ivanhoe's people

See answer #19

Sir Brian falls in love with Rebecca, but she wants nothing to do with him. Help her escape!

See answer #20

The Black Knight has come to rescue Ivanhoe! But what is the true identity of this hero? To find out, cross out the word CRUSADE wherever you see it.

CRUSADEKCRUSADE

ICRUSADENCRUSADEGCRUSADE

_K_ _i_ _n_ _g_

CRUSADERCRUSADEICRUSADE

CCRUSADEHCRUSADEA

CRUSADERCRUSADEDCRUSADE

_R_ _i_ _c_ _h_ _a_ _r_ _d_

See answer #21

The Adventures of Robin Hood

sherwoodforest

Robin Hood and his Merry Men fight injustice and help the poor in medieval England. To find out where they live, fold the page so the arrows meet.

See answer #22

The evil Sheriff of Nottingham is captured by Robin Hood! The embarrassed sheriff is sent home in rags. Can you find 5 differences between these two pictures?

See answer #23

The Sheriff of Nottingham tells Robin Hood to surrender if he wants to save Maid Marian. Follow the dots to see where she is being held captive.

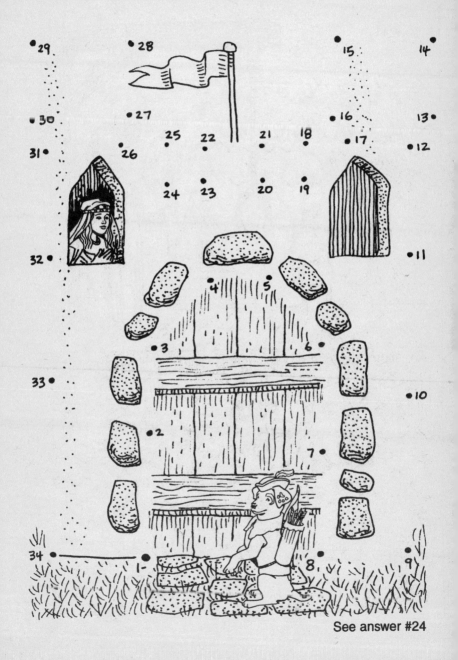

See answer #24

Robin Hood has been sentenced to hang! Can you find the Merry Men who have come to rescue him? They all wear feathered caps and are looking to the left for their signal!

See answer #25

The Count of Monte Cristo

Edmond Dantès is a sailor! Finish the bottom picture of Dantès so they match!

See answer #26

Dantès has won the heart of the lovely Mercedes, but Fernand is jealous. By reading every third letter (starting with "P"), you'll discover where Fernand wants to send Dantès.

START

Solution: ___ ___ ___ ___ ___ ___

See answer #27

Dantès is locked in the Chateau D'If even though he is innocent! While there, he meets the old Abbe Faria. Before the Abbe dies, he tells Dantès the location of a secret treasure. Can you help Dantès escape and find it?

See answer #28

Re-naming himself after the island where he found the treasure, Dantès becomes the mysterious Count of Monte Cristo. When he finally returns home, he has to face a terrible disappointment. Follow these directions to find out what!

Cross out COUNT OF from
MCEORUCNETDOEFS

Cross out MONTE from
MMAORNRTIEED

Cross out CRISTO from
FCERRINSATNOD

See answer #29

The Count of Monte Cristo is challenged to a duel after he exposes Fernand's evil past. Who is the young man who wants to fight? To find out, hold this page up to a mirror.

See answer #30

Treasure Island

Jim Hawkins has found a treasure map in Billy Bones' old sea chest! Solve this crossword puzzle about pirates.

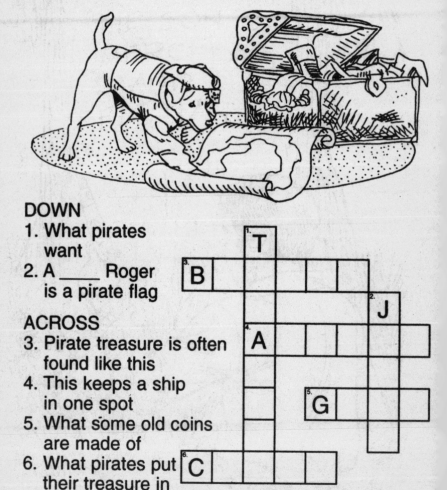

DOWN

1. What pirates want
2. A _____ Roger is a pirate flag

ACROSS

3. Pirate treasure is often found like this
4. This keeps a ship in one spot
5. What some old coins are made of
6. What pirates put their treasure in

See answer #31

Jim Hawkins is going to sail to Treasure Island.
Help him find his ship. It's the
one that's different from
all the rest.

See answer #32

Jim Hawkins overhears Long John Silver and his sidekick, Mr. Hands, plotting to steal the treasure map. To discover Long John Silver's profession, read the second letter of each word!

APPARENTLY, JIM'S FRIENDS FACE ATTACK NEXT!

_ _ _ _ _ _ _

See answer #33

Long John Silver has captured Jim and the map. While looking for the treasure, the pirate hears an eerie song! Connect the dots to see who he thinks is making the mysterious noise!

See answer #34

Long John Silver found only two guineas on Treasure Island. Jim Hawkins' friends found the real treasure. You can draw the angry Long John Silver by copying the lines in each square to the blank squares below.

See answer #35

The Red Badge of Courage

Young Henry Fielding marches off to fight in the Civil War. Can you find the twin soldiers?

See answer #36

Why is Henry running during his first battle? To learn the truth, color in the letters hidden in the trees.

See answer #37

Henry and his friends are part of the Union Army. Help Henry return to his regiment honorably by following the path that correctly spells UNION ARMY twice.

See answer #38

With his courage restored, Henry heroically captures the enemy flag. Can you circle 5 differences between the two flags?

See answer #39

Moby Dick

Ishmael is about to join the crew of a whaling ship! Unscramble these words and read down to learn the captain's name.

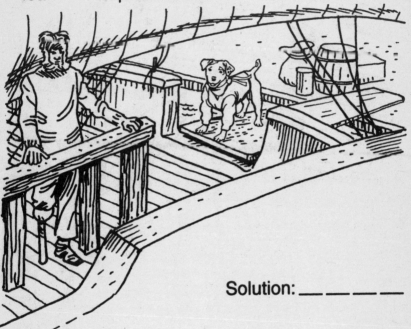

Solution: ___ ___ ___ ___

ALEWHS ___ ___ [ ] ___ ___ ___   *World's largest mammals*

NOPORHA [ ] ___ ___ ___ ___ ___ ___ ___   *A whaler's spear*

VESAW ___ [ ] ___ ___ ___   *The ocean makes these*

TOBA [ ] ___ ___ ___   *A small ship*

See answer #40

Captain Ahab is looking for Moby Dick, the white whale. How many whales can he see through his telescope?

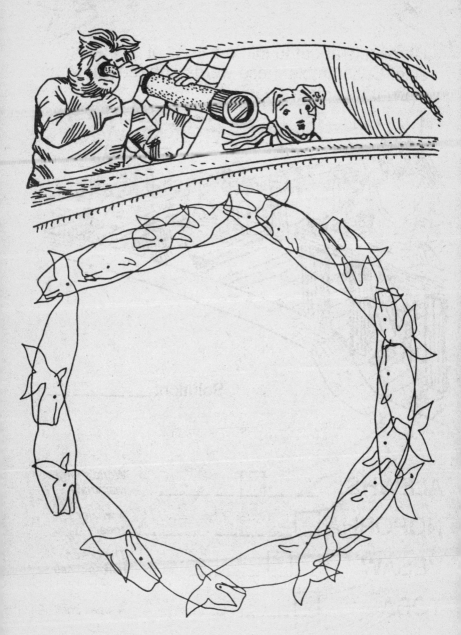

See answer #41

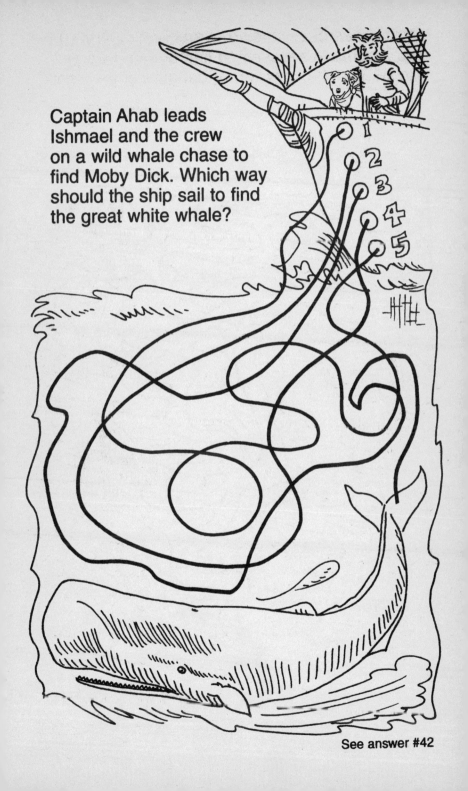

Captain Ahab leads Ishmael and the crew on a wild whale chase to find Moby Dick. Which way should the ship sail to find the great white whale?

See answer #42

Ishmael has been thrown overboard! Can you help him reach the floating timber so he won't drown? Watch out for other dangers of the deep!

See answer #43

Oliver Twist

Oliver Twist is a hungry orphan! Help him find the bowl of hot gruel with more. It's got a different design on it.

See answer #44

Alone on the streets of London, Oliver Twist makes friends with a young pickpocket. Solve the code to learn his name.

	A	B	C	D	E	F
1	D	Y	Z	R	C	G
2	X	A	L	J	P	U
3	R	M	E	O	H	Q
4	F	D	V	K	T	Y

B2 D1 E4 A4 F2 C2   B4 D3 A1 F1 C3 A3

See answer #45

Oliver is finally adopted into a loving family. How does he feel? Fill in all the squares with the number 1 in the grid below to find out.

See answer #46

Around the World in 80 Days

Phinias Fogg is an explorer. He wants to go around the world in record time! Can you find the right globe to help him chart his way?

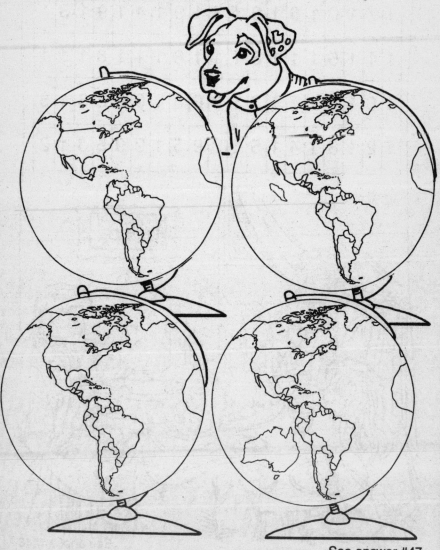

See answer #47

Connect the dots to see one of the vehicles Phinias Fogg will use on his journey around the world.

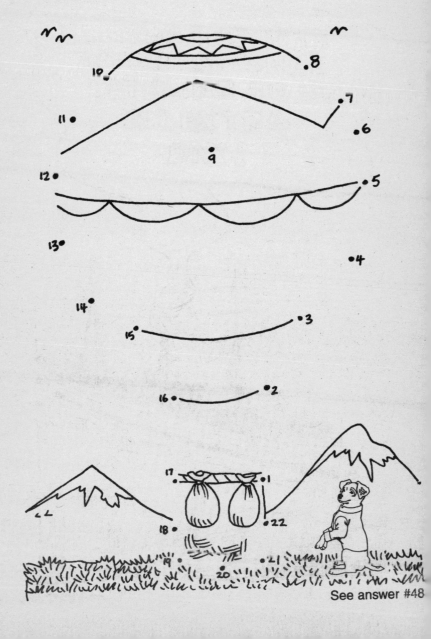

See answer #48

Will Phinias Fogg make it around the world in time? To find out how he completes his trip in 80 days, hold this page up to a mirror.

See answer #49

Phinias Fogg has made it around the world! What is he going to do now? Cross out the letters that spell FOGG whenever you see them to find out.

FGCOFEGGFOOGOLF
GOEFBGOFRFG
GAOFOTO
FFEOG!

Answer: ___ ___ ___ ___ ___ ___ ___ ___ ___ ___ ___

See answer #50

ANSWERS

#1

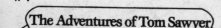

The Adventures of Tom Sawyer

Tom Sawyer and Huckleberry Finn sneak into the graveyard late one night and witness a crime. Unscramble the words below, and read down to see who wrote this American classic!

IDMIGHNT
M I D N I G H T
(The spookiest hour)

TARWS W A R T S
(Huck wants to cure these bumps)

SDARSKEN
D A R K N E S S
(What you find when there is no light)

HIIDGN H I D I N G
(What Tom and Huck are doing here)

MBTOTOSNE
T O M B S T O N E
(A grave marker)

MARK I W A I N

#2

Aunt Polly wonders what Tom Sawyer will explore today. Follow the path to help him get to school where he belongs!

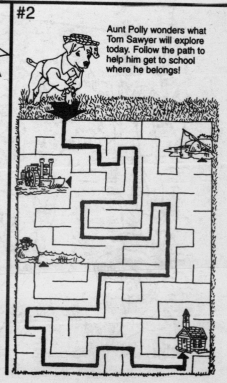

#3

Tom is on the witness stand because he knows who the real criminal is! Cross out the word TOM every time you see it to learn the culprit's name.

I N J U N

J O E

#4

Tom Sawyer and Becky Thatcher get lost in a cave! Can you help them find their way out?

#5

The Thousand and One Arabian Nights

The King of Persia orders beautiful Shahrazad to her doom! Wishbone wags his tail because he knows how she will cleverly save her own life. Fill in all the squares with a W, A, or G to discover what it is.

SHE MUST
TELL HIM
STORIES

#6

Ali Baba wants to learn the magic words that will open the secret cave of the Forty Thieves! Read up, down, backwards, forwards, and diagonally to find and circle the words on the list. The letters you *don't circle* will give Ali Baba his answer!

B A B A L I
C O P E N A
A F E I H T
V L T A L E
E Y T R O F
S E S A M E

ALI
BABA
CAVE
FORTY
THIEF
FLY
TALE
ATE

OPEN
SESAME

#7

Ali Baba's greedy brother Kasim forgot the secret words that will allow him to escape the cave! Follow the dots to see what Kasim had hoped to take with him.

#8

You'll find magic carpets in other stories from *The Thousand and One Arabian Nights*. Imagine Wishbone taking a ride on a flying carpet and then find the matching one.

#9

The Odyssey

Odysseus is sailing home after his victory in the Trojan War. Can you circle 5 differences between these two pictures?

#10

Tc keep Odysseus from leaving, the enchantress Circe has turned his men into pigs! Can you number the pictures in the right order to change them back?

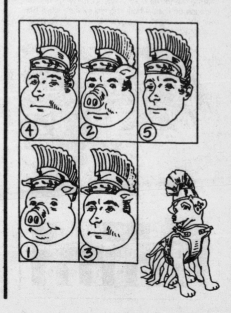

#11

Odysseus needs to hide his men from the Cyclops. Can you guess where they are hiding? Circle them.

#12

The Sirens sing to lure sailors onto the rocks. Odysseus has his men tie him to the mast so he can't answer their call. Can you count the number of singing Sirens?

10 SIRENS

#13

The Three Musketeers

D'Artagnan loves to practice fencing. Can you find all 6 swords in this picture? Circle them!

#14

The Three Musketeers help D'Artagnan battle the Cardinal's evil henchmen. Can you solve this crossword puzzle about the fine art of fencing?

DOWN
1. The Musketeers' home and capital of France
2. The sharp tip of a sword
3. Another name for sword

ACROSS
4. A Musketeer's weapon
5. The art of sword fighting

PARIS
SWORD
POINT
BLADE
FENCING

#15

The beautiful but evil Milady tries to win D'Artagnan over to the Cardinal's side, but he won't betray his friends! Fill in all the squares that have the letters F, I, N, or D to see what D'Artagnan wants to be.

#16

D'Artagnan has been accused of treason! The Cardinal will release him if he has a special document called a carte blanche. Can you help D'Artagnan find it?

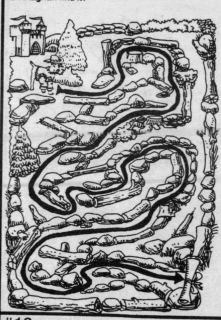

#17

Ivanhoe

Ivanhoe has just returned from the Crusades. Use the code on his shield to discover where he goes to show off his skills as a knight.

TOURNAMENT
OTIJGDQAGO

A=E   J=R   S=H
B=K   K=Q   T=O
C=P   L=X   U=Y
D=A   M=F   V=G
E=L   N=V   W=Z
F=I   O=T   X=W
G=N   P=C   Y=S
H=B   Q=M   Z=J
I=U   R=D

#18

Ivanhoe is a brave Saxon knight in medieval England. He has just beaten the Norman knight, Sir Brian, in archery and swordsmanship. Draw lines to match the weapons below to each other.

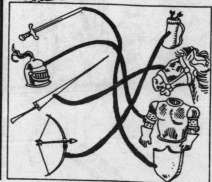

#19

Rebecca rescues Ivanhoe and takes him home in her caravan after he is wounded in the tournament. But he's not safe yet. Unscramble the words below, and then read the boxed letters to discover who is going to attack!

THE ATTACKER: __S I R   B R I A N__

WOSRD	S W O R D	A knight's weapon
DERI	R I D E	What knights do on horses
SEHOR	H O R S E	A knight's mount
AVERB	B R A V E	Not cowardly
ACCEBRE	R E B E C C A	Ivanhoe's new friend
HOEVNAI	I V A N H O E	The title of this novel
VESA	S A V E	To rescue
SNOXSA	S A X O N S	Ivanhoe's people

#20

Sir Brian falls in love with Rebecca, but she wants nothing to do with him. Help her escape!

#21

The Black Knight has come to rescue Ivanhoe! But what is the true identity of this hero? To find out, cross out the word CRUSADE wherever you see it.

K I N G

R I C H A R D

#22

The Adventures of Robin Hood

Robin Hood and his Merry Men fight injustice and help the poor in medieval England. To find out where they live, fold the page so the arrows meet.

SHERWOOD FOREST

#23

The evil Sheriff of Nottingham is captured by Robin Hood! The embarrassed sheriff is sent home in rags. Can you find 5 differences between these two pictures?

#24

The Sheriff of Nottingham tells Robin Hood to surrender if he wants to save Maid Marian. Follow the dots to see where she is being held captive.

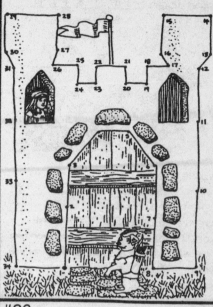

#25

Robin Hood has been sentenced to hang! Can you find the Merry Men who have come to rescue him! They all wear feathered caps and are looking to the left for their signal!

#26

The Count of Monte Cristo

Edmond Dantès is a sailor! Finish the bottom picture of Dantès so they match!

#27

Dantès has won the heart of the lovely Mercedes, but Fernand is jealous. By reading every third letter (starting with "P"), you'll discover where Fernand wants to send Dantès.

START

Solution: P R I S O N

#28

Dantès is locked in the Chateau D'If even though he is innocent! While there, he meets the old Abbe Faria. Before the Abbe dies, he tells Dantès the location of a secret treasure. Can you help Dantès escape and find it?

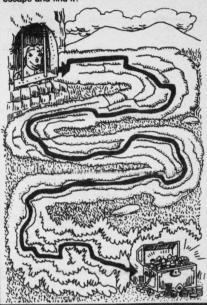

#29

Re-naming himself after the island where he found the treasure, Dantès becomes the mysterious Count of Monte Cristo. When he finally returns home, he has to face a terrible disappointment. Follow these directions to find out what!

Cross out COUNT OF from
MOECRCESDOEES

Cross out MONTE from
KMASRRTRIED

Cross out CRISTO from
FCEBRRINSANOD

#30

The Count of Monte Cristo is challenged to a duel after he exposes Fernand's evil past. Who is the young man who wants to fight? To find out, hold this page up to a mirror.

THE SON OF MERCEDES AND FERNAND

#31

Treasure Island

Jim Hawkins has found a treasure map in Billy Bones' old sea chest! Solve this crossword puzzle about pirates.

DOWN
1. What pirates want
2. A ____ Roger is a pirate flag

ACROSS
3. Pirate treasure is often found like this
4. This keeps a ship in one spot
5. What some old coins are made of
6. What pirates put their treasure in

Crossword answers:
- BURIED
- ANCHOR
- JOLLY
- GOLD
- CHEST
- TREASURE

#32

Jim Hawkins is going to sail to Treasure Island. Help him find his ship. It's the one that's different from all the rest.

#33

Jim Hawkins overhears Long John Silver and his sidekick, Mr. Hands, plotting to steal the treasure map. To discover Long John Silver's profession, read the second letter of each word!

APPARENTLY, JIM'S FRIENDS FACE ATTACK NEXT!

PIRATE

#34

Long John Silver has captured Jim and the map. While looking for the treasure, the pirate hears an eerie song! Connect the dots to see who he thinks is making the mysterious noise!

#35

Long John Silver found only two guineas on Treasure Island. Jim Hawkins' friends found the real treasure. You can draw the angry Long John Silver by copying the lines in each square to the blank squares below.

#36

The Red Badge of Courage

Young Henry Fielding marches off to fight in the Civil War. Can you find the twin soldiers?

#37

Why is Henry running during his first battle? To learn the truth, color in the letters hidden in the trees.

#38

Henry and his friends are part of the Union Army. Help Henry return to his regiment honorably by following the path that correctly spells UNION ARMY twice.

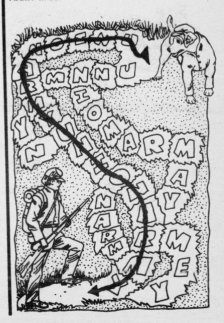

#39

With his courage restored, Henry heroically captures the enemy flag. Can you circle 5 differences between the two flags?

#40

Moby Dick

Ishmael is about to join the crew of a whaling ship! Unscramble these words and read down to learn the captain's name.

Solution: A H A B

ALEWHS	W H A L E S	World's largest mammals
NOPORHA	H A R P O O N	A whaler's spear
VESAW	W A V E S	The ocean makes these
TOBA	B O A T	A small ship

#41

Captain Ahab is looking for Moby Dick, the white whale. How many whales can he see through his telescope?

15

#42

Captain Ahab leads Ishmael and the crew on a wild whale chase to find Moby Dick. Which way should the ship sail to find the great white whale?

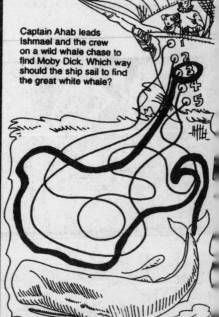

43

Ishmael has been thrown overboard! Can you help him reach the floating timber so he won't drown? Watch out for other dangers of the deep!

#44

Oliver Twist

Oliver Twist is a hungry orphan! Help him find the bowl of hot gruel with more. It's got a different design on it.

45

One on the streets of London, Oliver Twist makes friends with a young pickpocket. Solve the code to learn his name.

	A	B	C	D	E	F
1	D	Y	Z	R	C	G
2	X	A	L	J	P	U
3	R	M	E	O	H	Q
4	F	D	V	K	T	Y

A R T F U L   D O D G E R
B2 D1 E4 A4 F2 C2   B4 D3 A1 F1 C3 A3

#46

Oliver is finally adopted into a loving family. How does he feel? Fill in all the squares with the number 1 in the grid below to find out.

#47

Around the World in 80 Days

Phinias Fogg is an explorer. He wants to go around the world in record time! Can you find the right globe to help him chart his way?

#48

Connect the dots to see one of the vehicles Phinias Fogg will use on his journey around the world.

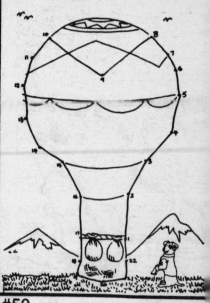

#49

Will Phinias Fogg make it around the world in time? To find out how he completes his trip in 80 days, hold this page up to a mirror.

#50

Phinias Fogg has made it around the world! What is he going to do now? Cross out the letters that spell FOGG whenever you see them to find out.

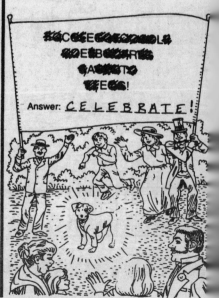

Answer: CELEBRATE!